A GUIDED JOURNAL

for

Caregivers

MARION KARPINSKI, RN

A Division of Health Care Training Systems, Inc.

A special thanks to Gaea Yudron who contributed to the writing and copyediting of this journal. Gaea has worked in the field of holistic health and wellness for 30 years and willingly shared her wisdom.

Thank you to Debbie Thornley, poetry therapist, who shared her experience on the therapeutic value of poetry and journal writing.

Thank you to Debi Dieterich for inspiring me to write the journal.

Cover photograph: Mike Karpinski

Design: Robert Frost

INTRODUCTION

A Guided Journal for Caregivers provides a variety of tools to help caregivers reduce stress, increase well-being and enjoy creative expression. A journal provides a safe place to express our innermost feelings, concerns, hopes and dreams. Journaling allows us to discover different parts of ourselves and to give voice to what really matters. It has been shown that writing about events that affect us deeply and expressing how we feel about them improves mental and physical health. The journal is also a place where we can celebrate the humor and tenderness of life: a place to record precious moments. These are some of the reasons why many people view their journal as a supportive friend along life's path. To get the most out of journaling, date each entry. Keep what you write so that you can reflect upon it later. Write only for yourself, and do not judge what you write. Include photographs, cherished letters or cards in the pages of your journal to mark those special times.

"There's no right way of writing. There's only your way."

– MILTON LOMASK

*"The future belongs to those
who believe in the beauty of their dreams."*

– ELEANOR ROOSEVELT

Each one of us has unique experiences, memories, activities and places that bring us joy or give us a feeling of well-being. Think about what brings you joy and write about it here...

Joy is the simplest form of gratitude.

– KARL BARTH

Even in the most challenging times, there is always something to be grateful for. Take a moment to think of some of the things in your life that you can be grateful for and write about them here…

*"The first rule is to keep an untroubled spirit.
The second is to look things in the face and know
them for what they are."*

— MARCUS AURELIUS

Writing about your feelings can be a very healing experience.
It is important not to deny or judge how you feel. What are your
feelings today?

Our feelings contain important messages. When we take time to listen to those messages we can develop positive solutions that support our well-being. What messages are your feelings trying to communicate to you?

_____

_____

_____

_____

_____

_____

_____

_____

_____

_____

_____

_____

_____

_____

_____

_____

_____

_____

_____

_____

_____

_____

*"In order to have a real relationship with our creativity,
we must take the time and care to cultivate it."*

– JULIA CAMERON

Writing non-stop without editing or censoring can be a freeing experience. This kind of writing stimulates creativity and can help us discover new things about ourselves in a spontaneous way. Set a timer for 3 or 5 minutes and begin writing. Do not lift the pen from the paper. Do not stop, just keep writing whatever comes to your mind…

"How far you go in life depends on you being tender with the young, compassionate with the aged, sympathetic with the striving and tolerant of the weak and the strong. Because someday in life you will have been all of these."

— GEORGE WASHINGTON CARVER

A Key Figure

Of everyone you have met in your life, who is the person that has inspired you the most? What are the personal qualities that you most admire in that person? How has that person influenced your life?

_____

_____

_____

_____

_____

_____

_____

_____

_____

_____

_____

_____

_____

Often we have the same qualities as the people we most admire. What are your greatest gifts and strengths? Notice whether they are similar to the person who most inspires you. Are there other qualities you would like to develop?

_____

_____

_____

_____

_____

_____

_____

_____

_____

_____

_____

_____

_____

_____

_____

_____

_____

_____

_____

"Each moment of the year has its own beauty ...
a picture which was never before and shall never be seen again."

– RALPH WALDO EMERSON

Capturing Precious Moments

In the midst of caregiving, we are often so focused on providing care that we don't take time to record the tender moments that we share with one another. These are the true gifts of caregiving. Writing the precious moments down will provide you with a keepsake in the years to come. Take several deep breaths and allow your body and mind to relax. Think of a positive time you shared with the person for whom you are caring. Write a description of that time in either prose or poetry. At the end of the journal there are more pages to write about other precious moments.

_____

_____

_____

_____

_____

_____

_____

_____

_____

_____

"As I write I create myself again and again."

– JOY HARJO

Write about the positive things you have learned about yourself from being a caregiver...

_____

_____

_____

_____

_____

_____

_____

_____

_____

_____

_____

_____

_____

_____

_____

_____

_____

_____

_____

Things that are easy for me to handle as a caregiver are:

What I can't handle as a caregiver is:

Review your list of what you can't handle. Notice which items you can change and those that are beyond your ability to change. How can you let go of the things that are beyond your ability to change?

_____

_____

_____

_____

_____

_____

_____

_____

_____

_____

_____

_____

_____

_____

_____

_____

_____

_____

_____

_____

A Tool for Finding Solutions

Identify the most pressing problem in the list of things you can't handle that you have the ability to change. Begin to write every solution that you can think of to resolve the problem. The list should contain at least 20 items. Then choose 1-3 items that provide the easiest and best solution. If those don't work after you have tried them, continue down the list until you find one that does. This is a tool you can use for other challenges you face.

Write what you think and feel now. Not what happened yesterday or not what you have to do today. Write how you feel at this moment...

"We cannot do everything at once,
but we can do something at once."

– CALVIN COOLIDGE

Stress is part of everyday life. We cannot eliminate stress in our lives but we can learn ways to manage it. The first step is to recognize the warning signs of stress, which can be different for each person.

Here are some common warning signs of stress that caregivers experience.

• High levels of fear or anxiety
• Feeling irritable or out of control
• Resenting the person you are caring for
• Overeating or undereating
• Feeling trapped
• Insomnia or sleeping too much
• Chronic fatigue
• Excessive use of drugs, alcohol, or sugary foods
• Difficulty with concentration or decision-making
• Withdrawing from people
• Feeling hopeless

Take a moment to think about your own warning signs of stress.

My warning signs of stress are...

Once you recognize the warning signs of stress, the next step is to identify the cause of stress in order to find solutions.

What causes stress for you?

A Tool for Finding Solutions

Of the causes you have listed, which creates the most stress for you?
Begin to write every solution that you can think of to reduce that stress.
The list should contain at least 20 items. Then choose 1-3 items that
provide the easiest and best solution. If those don't work, continue
down the list until you find one that does.

_____

_____

_____

_____

_____

_____

_____

_____

_____

_____

_____

_____

_____

_____

_____

_____

_____

_____

"Listening creates holy silence. Listening is like the rain."

- RACHEL NAOMI REMEN

Take 10-15 minutes to relax in a comfortable place. It could be in your home or it could be in a natural setting. Simply listen. If there are ambient sounds, just listen without judgment. Relax into inner stillness. If thoughts or concerns arise, just let them go. You can always return to them later. For now, just take a respite in the openness of listening.

When you are done, you can write about your experience.

_____

_____

_____

_____

_____

_____

_____

_____

_____

_____

_____

_____

_____

_____

_____

"Light tomorrow with today."

– ELIZABETH BARRETT BROWNING

Joy is a choice. What can I choose today that will bring me joy?

_____

_____

_____

_____

_____

_____

_____

_____

_____

_____

_____

_____

_____

_____

_____

_____

_____

_____

_____

"It is never too late—in fiction or in life—to revise."

– NANCY THAYER

Making an Emotion into a Character

Choose an emotion to work with. The first time you do this exercise, pick an emotion that you find difficult in your present day-to-day life, such as anger, frustration or hopelessness. What kind of a character do you imagine this emotion to be? Is it male or female, old or young, quiet or loud? What color represents it best? Is it human, animal, plant, mineral or something else? What does the character want to say? What does the character wish for? Write about the emotion from this perspective.

"Forgive all who have offended you, not for them, but for yourself."

— HARRIET UTS NELSON

One of the keys to wellness is the willingness to let go of people or situations that have caused us pain. Releasing the past in this way does not mean it never happened, but in letting go, we free ourselves of the pain.

What could I release today that would help me take better care of myself?

_____

_____

_____

_____

_____

_____

_____

_____

_____

_____

_____

_____

_____

_____

_____

Action Plan

Take a moment to think of one or two things that refresh you and tha
you would like to include regularly in your life. Make sure that your
choices are simple enough to achieve fairly easily.

Then, create an action plan that will help you bring these activities
into your life on a regular basis. Use one action plan for each activity

Creating an action plan is simple. For example, if you want to
include a walk with your neighbor once a week, then write that activity
with a specific starting date and the steps you need to take to make
that happen. It should look something like this:

To help me begin walking with my neighbor by
Wednesday, June 12th, I will:

1. Check with my neighbor to find a time what works for both of us.

2. Call my sister and ask her if she could watch Mom once a week
   for one hour.

3. If my sister cannot help out, then I will call the local respite services.

4. Buy myself a pair of good walking shoes.

Then sign and date your agreement with yourself. It can be helpful to
have your action plan in a place where you will see it everyday. You
can copy the page from your journal or rewrite the steps on a separate
piece of paper. Work on it step by step. This is an effective way to
reach the goals you set in caring for yourself.

Action Plan #1

To help me begin (activity) _____
_____

by (day & date) _____
_____

I will:

1. _____
_____
_____
_____

2. _____
_____
_____
_____

3. _____
_____
_____
_____

4. _____
_____
_____
_____

Signed: _____ Date: _____

Action Plan #2

To help me begin (activity) _____

_____

by (day & date) _____

_____

I will:

1. _____

_____

_____

_____

2. _____

_____

_____

_____

3. _____

_____

_____

_____

4. _____

_____

_____

_____

Signed: _____   Date: _____

"If I keep a green bough in my heart, the singing bird will come."

— CHINESE PROVERB

A Laughing Matter

Laughter is not only fun, but may be one of the healthiest things you can do. Laughter, like crying, is a form of catharsis, providing an outlet for feelings of stress and anxiety. Laughter can help clear your head, so that you can look at a situation from a new angle.

Studies show that laughter causes a temporary increase in heart rate and blood pressure, which aids in delivery of oxygen and nutrients to your entire body. Laughter can also help relax tense muscles in your face, shoulders and torso. Laughter helps the body produce new immune cells faster. Several studies have shown that exposing people to humorous experiences significantly increases their ability to deal with pain. When you laugh, your brain releases endorphins — the body's natural painkillers.

How can you include laughter into your life more often?
Here are some suggestions:

1. Find five things to laugh at today.

2. Put funny movies or comedy shows into your schedule on a regular basis.

3. Get together with a friend and laugh together. It doesn't even require funny jokes or events. Just start laughing together, and enjoy the contagious, exhilarating qualities of laughter.

4. Remember the funniest events in your life.

Even during stressful and difficult times, I can find moments of humor. What can I find to laugh about today?

"He who laughs, lasts."

– MARY POOLE

Remember one or more times in your life when you really laughed. Write about what you enjoyed about those moments. Is there a way for you to bring that kind of feeling into your life today?

_____

_____

_____

_____

_____

_____

_____

_____

_____

_____

_____

_____

_____

_____

_____

_____

A Letter

In the busyness of our everyday life, we may not set aside the time to express our deeper feelings to the person for whom we are providing care. It may not be possible to communicate easily, because of Alzheimer's or other illnesses. Writing a letter to the person you are caring for can be very healing because it allows you to express what you are really feeling. Take time to write a letter to your care recipient. Give yourself permission to write whatever you feel even if the feeling is not a positive one...

Abdominal Breathing

In stressful situations, people tend to take in shallow breaths that fill only the top portion of the lungs. This is referred to as chest breathing. Relaxed abdominal breathing fills our lungs completely, giving us the energy and oxygen we need. It also naturally reduces stress and body tension.

Before you begin writing in your journal today, take 3 -5 minutes to practice abdominal breathing. Begin by lying on a firm flat surface such as a mat, floor, or firm mattress. Place one hand on your abdomen just below the navel and the other hand on your chest. Breathe naturally and notice whether your breath raises your chest, abdomen or both. Now place both hands on your abdomen and focus your breath there. As you breathe in, your breath should fill your abdomen and you will notice it rise. Allow yourself to relax more and more with each breath, the way a small child relaxes when resting. Abdominal breathing is a great stress reduction technique that you can use anywhere.

"All my life through, the new sights of nature made me rejoice like a child."

— MARIE CURIE

Nature

Even brief journeys into Nature can be soothing and revitalizing. Walking in a park, through a field, or sitting beneath a tree gives us time to let go of the focused attention that caregiving often demands. Being in Nature gives us needed time for quiet aloneness and inner stillness. Think about how much time you set aside to be in Nature.

What are your favorite places in Nature and when you are there, how do you feel?

_____

_____

_____

_____

_____

_____

_____

_____

_____

_____

_____

"The real voyage of discovery consists not in seeking new landscapes, but in having new eyes."

– MARCEL PROUST

What happened today that moved you, touched you, or made you laugh?

When we become a caregiver, we sometimes forget that there is not just one person who needs care. There are two. The person receiving care and the person providing care—the caregiver.
It is important as caregivers to recognize that we too have needs and the right to fulfill those needs. What are your needs?

_____

_____

_____

_____

_____

_____

_____

_____

_____

_____

_____

_____

_____

_____

_____

_____

_____

Knowing that I am responsible for meeting my own needs,
what steps can I take to fulfill some of the things I need most?
This could include asking others for help.

"Life must be lived as play."

– PLATO

Playfulness and pleasure are a vital part of life. Think of some of the playful moments you have enjoyed in your life. What did you enjoy most about them? Who were you with and what were the circumstances?

_____

_____

_____

_____

_____

_____

_____

_____

_____

_____

_____

_____

_____

_____

_____

_____

If you could create a character of your playfulness,
what would he/she be like?

_____

_____

_____

_____

_____

_____

_____

_____

_____

What words describe my playful character?

_____

_____

_____

_____

_____

_____

_____

_____

_____

_____

_____

_____

_____

_____

What colors describe my playful character?

_____

_____

_____

_____

_____

_____

_____

_____

What actions or activities describe my playful character?

_____

_____

_____

_____

_____

_____

_____

_____

_____

_____

What sounds or music describe my playful character?

_____

_____

_____

_____

_____

_____

_____

_____

_____

What movements describe my playful character?

_____

_____

_____

_____

_____

_____

_____

_____

_____

_____

_____

"The only way to have a friend is to be one."

– RALPH WALDO EMERSON

Maintaining the close friendships we have formed in our life gives us a sense of well-being and support. We can share things with close friends that we can't always share with family members. Our true friends accept us through all of life's ups and downs. It is important for our well-being to continue our friendships rather than let them go because of the demands of caregiving. Caregivers who give up relationships that are meaningful to them are at a greater risk for depression, isolation and health problems.

Who is your closest friend and why is that friendship meaningful to you?

_____

_____

_____

_____

_____

_____

_____

_____

_____

_____

_____

Sometimes friends and neighbors will ask how they can help, but you may not always know what to suggest. Keeping a list of your current needs makes it easier for you to tell them the ways that they can help. The list gives them an opportunity to choose a particular task that they can do. Your list can include errands, such as shopping or going to the pharmacy, respite, making a meal, or transportation, etc.

Write a list of the needs you have now. Make a copy of it to keep handy when someone asks how he/she can help. Keep the list current.

_____

_____

_____

_____

_____

_____

_____

_____

_____

_____

_____

_____

_____

_____

_____

What are some other sources of support in your life? These could be community, church, family, friends, clubs, neighbors, support groups, etc.

_____

_____

_____

_____

_____

_____

_____

_____

_____

_____

_____

_____

_____

_____

_____

_____

_____

_____

_____

_____

_____

_____

When I get a break from caregiving, these are some of the things I would like to do...

_____

_____

_____

_____

_____

_____

_____

_____

_____

_____

_____

_____

_____

_____

_____

_____

_____

_____

_____

_____

_____

_____

A journal is a safe place to express yourself. You can vent feelings such as anger without hurting anyone.

_____

_____

_____

_____

_____

_____

_____

_____

_____

_____

_____

_____

_____

_____

_____

_____

_____

_____

_____

_____

How can I recognize and manage my anger or frustration in healthy ways? Some examples could be:

Count to 10, Go for a walk, Write in my journal...

"Nothing can bring you peace but yourself."

– RALPH WALDO EMERSON

A common caregiver belief is: I can't help how I feel. I have no
control over it. The truth is that what happens to us is not nearly
as important as how we respond to it. We are free to choose new
attitudes, even when circumstances may be challenging.

What can I choose to change about my attitudes?

_____

_____

_____

_____

_____

_____

_____

_____

_____

_____

_____

_____

_____

"Perfectionism is a dangerous state of mind in an imperfect world."

– ROBERT HILYER

Many caregivers think that they must do everything perfectly, but demanding constant perfection of oneself creates stress. To challenge the belief that you must do everything perfectly, ask yourself: is that how I learned other skills like riding a bike or making lasagna? Most likely you'll find that it took time to learn a new skill and you learned by trial and error.

So you need to look at caregiving the same way. It's a learning process that changes from day to day. Rather than expecting yourself to do everything perfectly, give yourself permission to learn as you go, and even to make mistakes along the way.

In what ways can I let go of being the perfect caregiver?

_____

_____

_____

_____

_____

_____

_____

Every person's life has significant turning points.
What are some turning points in your life?

Here, we end the structured exercises in this guided journal. The remainder of these pages are open. On them, you can repeat some of the exercises given throughout the book, or simply use the pages for your own journal entries...

"We make a living by what we get,
but we make a life by what we give."

— SIR WINSTON CHURCHILL

"Nothing happens unless first a dream."

– CARL SANDBURG

"There will be enough time to do it all but not all at once."

– WAYNE SOTILE

"You gain strength, experience and confidence by every experience where you really stop to look fear in the face. You must do the thing you cannot do."

– ELEANOR ROOSEVELT

"I have always set personal boundaries of what is funny and what is not. I have been quoted as saying 'There are just some things you don't poke fun at.' I was wrong. Laughter rises out of tragedy when you need it the most and rewards you for your courage."

– ERMA BOMBECK

*"Expressing your enthusiasm can add years
of creative life to your time on earth."*

— MARSHA SINETAR

*"Authentic success is reaching the point
where being is as important as doing."*

– S ARAH B AN B REATHNACH

"Some men see things as they are and ask why.
Others dream things that never were and ask why not."

– GEORGE BERNARD SHAW

Tomorrow I was
Going to the spring meadows
To pick the young greens.
It snowed all day yesterday
And snowed all day today.

                   – A K A H I T O

*"Life is 10 percent what you make it,
and 90 percent how you take it."*

– IRVING BERLIN

"Writing is the ax that breaks the frozen sea within us."

— FRANZ KAFKA